WHO
KNOWS
TEN?

WHO   KNO

WS TEN?

Children's Tales of the
Ten Commandments

Told by MOLLY CONE

Illustrated by URI SHULEVITZ

**UNION OF AMERICAN
HEBREW CONGREGATIONS**

LIBRARY OF
CONGRESS CATALOGUE
NUMBER 65-24639

PRODUCED IN THE U. S. OF AMERICA

EDITOR'S INTRODUCTION

In *The Process of Education,* a classic of contemporary educational theory, Jerome Bruner, of Harvard University, argues that the essentials of any subject can be taught to any one at any age in some intellectually honest form, and that, as a consequence, we need not waste precious school years by postponing the teaching of important subjects on the ground that they are too difficult.

Molly Cone heeds his admonition and proves his point. Her stories about the Ten Commandments—tastefully selected and gracefully told—provide us with the means for transmitting significant ideas of Judaism to our younger students.

There is good reason, therefore, why her work should gain acceptance, giving its young readers both instruction and inspiration in their early religious school experience.

A successful writer since her student days at the University of Washington, Mrs. Cone has authored some twelve books published for children. She is an active member of Seattle's Temple Beth Am, and it is her interest in its religious school which led her to the writing of books for Jewish children, beginning with *Stories of Jewish Symbols* which appeared in print last year.

RABBI ALEXANDER M. SCHINDLER

ACKNOWLEDGEMENTS

THE IDEA FOR THIS BOOK CAME FROM RABBI ALEXANDER M. SCHINDLER, *Director of Education,* Commission on Jewish Education, Union of American Hebrew Congregations, whose inspiration is here gratefully acknowledged. A special word also for JEANETTE SCHRIEBER, who shared in the planning and contributed to the ideas from which this book took form.

My thanks also to Rayanna Simons of the UAHC for her editorial help, and to the members of the Commission who read the book and contributed their expert knowledge to its realization; Rabbi Daniel J. Silver, Rabbi David I. Cedarbaum, Mr. Alan D. Bennett, Mrs. Ruth Gruber and Mrs. Sylvia Goldman. I should also like to acknowledge gratefully the skill and taste with which Ralph Davis, Production Manager for the UAHC, has assembled the book. And to the Union's proofreading department headed by Mrs. Josette Knight, my warm appreciation for their painstaking work in the proofreading and final corrections of the manuscript.

Acknowledgements

I am, of course, most grateful to Mr. Uri Schulevitz, the talented artist, for his great contribution to the book. Mr. Shulevitz is the author-illustrator of *The Moon in My Room*. He is the illustrator, among other books, for *The Mystery of the Woods* by Mary Stolz and *Charlie Sang a Song* by H. R. and Daniel Hayes. All of the above have been published by Harper and Row. He also illustrated the *Haggadah for the School* published by the United Synagogue.

"The Reminder" adapted from *A Servant When He Reigns,* Page 172, *Folktales of Israel,* Copyright University of Chicago.

"A Place Called Kushta" adapted from a talmudic tale, page 398, *A Rabbinic Anthology,* C. G. Montefiore and H. Loewe, The World Publishing Company.

"The Sweetest Sound" adapted from *What Melody is the Sweetest?,* Page 172, *Folktales of Israel,* Copyright University of Chicago.

"The Rabbi's Eye" adapted from *Seek Peace,* Page 148, *The Jewish Caravan,* Copyright 1935, Leo W. Schwarz.

"The Reward" and "The Gossip" adapted from folktales of Jewish origin.

"The Peach, the Pitcher and the Fur Coat," adapted in part from *Anatomy of Leadership,* Page 147, *The Jewish Caravan,* Copyright 1935, Leo W. Schwarz.

WHAT'S INSIDE?

ONCE, IN a puzzle store, I found a little box. Inside it there was another box, and inside that was another one. Each box was complete, each was perfect, and each was different in size and color from the one before.

In this book, you will find the Ten Commandments. If you look into the meaning of each commandment, you will find another meaning. And if you look inside that, you may find still another—and so on.

Like the box inside the box in the puzzle store, there is meaning inside meaning in each commandment. And it is strange how many people there are who look at the Ten Commandments, yet have never discovered the meanings within them.

In a way, this book is a puzzle book. It gives you a chance to find for yourself the many meanings inside each commandment. Each chapter tells you a story, and each story gives you a truth. Each truth holds inside it something else, which perhaps you never thought of before.

But the story doesn't end there. If you think about it, you will see that what it says has something to do with what is happening every day around you—in your home, your school and your neighborhood. The way to discover how far the story goes is to talk about the ideas in it with your teacher and your classmates, and with your friends and your family.

You will find that many of these ideas are the very questions that people everywhere in the world are talking about today. Talking with people about them and hearing what other people think will help you to think, too.

And when you have come to the end of the stories in this book . . .

And thus have discovered many of the meanings inside the meanings inside the commandments . . .

You will know

SOMETHING IMPORTANT.

You will know how to do justice, and what is good. And by living this way, you will help to make a world of people who respect and understand each other.

THE AUTHOR

IN
THIS
BOOK

"WHO WILL HEAR?"

LONG AGO, the story is told, a Great Voice rose from a mountain top and called out to all the nations of people on the earth.

"Who will hear?" the Great Voice spoke.

At the sound, it is said, no bird sang, no ox lowed, the ocean did not roar, and no creature stirred.

In the breathless silence all the peoples of the world listened to the words of the Ten Commandments.

However, as it is told, although all the nations of the world listened, they did not hear. For not one of them wanted to change their way of life to follow the Lord's words.

Not one of them, that is, except a wandering band of people who were not a nation at all. They were slaves who had come from the land of Egypt. They were the Israelites. They had once lived in the land of Canaan. When famine struck they had moved to the land of Egypt. There they lived for many years in peace and plenty, until a cruel Pharaoh made all the Israelites in his country slaves.

Moses led them out of slavery. He led them out of the land of Egypt into the wilderness, in search of freedom.

There, in the middle of the desert, at the foot of the mountain of Sinai, the wandering people heard the thunder and saw the fire and the smoke. Moses scratched onto two tablets of stone the words God called out to all the peoples of the world.

"WHO WILL HEAR?" the Great Voice had said. The Israelites listened. And they heard . . .

I

I AM
THE LORD YOUR GOD
WHO BROUGHT YOU
OUT OF THE
LAND OF EGYPT,
OUT OF THE
HOUSE OF BONDAGE

I

I AM
THE LORD YOUR GOD

WITH THEIR ears, the Israelites heard the voice of Moses reading from the tablets of stone. But with their hearts they were hearing the words of God. They crowded around Moses and the tablets he held.

They were free, the First Commandment said. Hearing this, the Israelites thought they could forget they had lived as slaves in Egypt. The thin trees on the mountain side began to shake with their shouts of joy.

At their shouts, the words of the commandment on the tablets of stone seemed to turn to fire. The Israelites stopped shouting. They stepped back and shielded their eyes with their hands. But they couldn't seem to shut out the flames. In silence, the people stared through their fingers at the words of the First Commandment.

Then they began to understand what the commandment was really saying. God gave life, it said, and with it God also gave freedom. Life and freedom were part of the same commandment because God meant them to go together in His world.

"Oh!" said the Israelites. They took their hands away from their eyes and looked at each other. What the First Commandment was really saying was that every person God created had the same right to freedom.

"It means we must never take freedom for ourselves alone," one of the wanderers said.

The Israelites nodded. They remembered how they had lived as slaves in Egypt. They remembered—and they promised themselves never to forget.

The Reminder

IN A CERTAIN kingdom, long ago, the people followed a strange custom. When a king died, a royal bird was sent out. The bird flew around. And the person on whose head the bird came to rest was named king. That's the way it was done in this kingdom.

One time a very curious thing happened.

In this kingdom there was a slave who made the fine people of the court laugh, even though his face was sad. They thought he was so funny that they dressed him in a cap of chicken feathers, and a belt made of lamb's hooves, and gave him a little drum to beat.

One night, the slave dreamed that a small voice whispered to him. He sat up and tried to remember what the voice had said. But all that came to his head was the soft sound—*seeeeds.*

"Seeds? How strange," he thought. What could it mean? All the next day, he puzzled over the strange dream. He could not make any sense of it.

That evening, as he was putting on his hat of chicken feathers, he saw that a number of small seeds had stuck to his feet. Quickly he scooped them up, and because he didn't know what to do with them, he put them into the crown of his hat. Then he ran upstairs to make the people laugh.

But the people of the court did not laugh at him that night. They did not feel like laughing, not even at the funny slave. For their king was dead.

The sad-faced slave crept around behind the king's empty chair and fell asleep. He slept sitting up, with his elbows on his knees and his chin in his hands. And he didn't wake up until he heard a curious sound in the air.

Rubbing his eyes, he peered around. He saw a great bird flying through the castle halls.

He opened his eyes wide, for he had never seen a bird like this before. It was so large that the flapping of its wings sent a breeze through the castle rooms.

The bird flew around the room once. It came so close it almost touched the slave. Hastily he pulled out of the way. Then, on his hands and knees behind the king's empty chair, he ventured to look out again.

The bird flew around the room a second time. The slave crawled out a bit to see it better.

The bird flew around the room the third time—and landed on the head of the slave.

"Ouch!" said he, trying to push it off. "Shoo! Get away from me!" But the bird sitting on his cap of chicken

feathers had found the seeds. He sat there and pecked
at them greedily.

A great cry arose from the people. "The king!" they
shouted. "The king!"

Suddenly the slave felt many hands upon him. He was
lifted high and placed on the king's throne.

"Long live the king!" the ladies and gentlemen of the court shouted, and they all bowed low before him.

"Me?" stuttered the slave. "But I am only a slave!"

They paid no attention to what he said. For the great bird was sitting calmly on his cap of feathers, like an eagle in its nest.

"O king!" said the minister. "You have been chosen by the Royal Bird. You will rule over our land for the rest of your life. But you must promise one thing."

"What is that?" asked the astonished slave.

"You must never forget that you are king!"

The new king slowly nodded, and all the people clapped. The trumpets blew and everyone shouted.

The king who had been a slave sat up in his high throne, but his face was still sad.

"Build me a hut," he said without a smile. "Build it right outside the palace door."

Puzzled, the minister ordered a small house to be built just outside the great palace door.

The king directed the workmen to make it a simple hut. It was made of rough wood, and had no windows. The door was a stout one, however, and on it the king himself placed a huge lock.

The people of the court walked back and forth, looking at it curiously. When the hut was built, the new king entered it. He stayed only a few minutes. When he came out, he locked the door behind him.

Every year this king issued new laws. One year he decreed that every slave should be set free after working six years. Another year he decreed that a slave should be paid for the work he did, and that he could buy his freedom from his master with the money he earned. Quietly, one day, the king decreed that in this certain kingdom, no man had the right to own another. All who lived there were free men; there were no more slaves. And the king's face was no longer sad. More and more, the people saw him smile.

But so gradually did these changes come about, that the people of his kingdom hardly noticed.

What they did notice was the king's custom of going into the little hut once every year.

One day the minister asked, "What are you guarding so closely in that little house?"

"Inside are my most treasured possessions," the king said. "See for yourself." He unlocked the door and stepped aside.

In great eagerness the minister went into the tiny hut. He came out again shaking his head. "But I see only a feather cap, a belt of lamb's hooves and a drum!"

"That's right," the king said, smiling. "I made a promise to you that I would never forget I was king. But at the same time, I made a promise to God never to forget I once was a slave."

And carefully locking the door of the little hut, he went back into his palace.

10

II

YOU
SHALL HAVE
NO OTHER GODS
— ONLY *ME*

II

YOU
SHALL HAVE
NO OTHER GODS
— ONLY *ME*

AT THE words of the Second Commandment, the Israelites covered their heads with their arms. What they saw was lightning, and what they heard was thunder. But they were not sure, and were afraid.

Was the fire God? They wondered. Or was He part of the great sound? Was God in the smoke that poured from the mountain top?

Where was God? They tried to see His face in the sky but all they could see was the smoke, the fire, the clouds and the lightning.

Uneasily, the Israelites looked at each other. If God was nothing they could see, how would they know Him? Where would they find Him?

An old man murmured:

"Hear O Israel, the Lord our God, the Lord is One . . ."

The Israelites bent their heads. They told themselves they must think about the commandment and think about God. Earnestly they set themselves to thinking.

They thought about themselves, instead, and about their freedom and their joy.

"I must think about God," each told himself, firmly.

But what they thought about then was each other.

Quickly each looked up and around. In every face all saw the same wonder. Thinking of each other, they had each felt closer to God.

That was when they found the answer to their question. All at once they knew how God could be seen.

The Princess Who Wanted to See God

ONCE THERE was a princess who had never cried. She had never had anything to cry about. Whatever in the world she wanted, she got. One day she woke up and said that she wanted to see God.

"God?" shouted her father. "You mean GOD? Don't be silly, child. No one in the whole world has seen God."

Princess Eleanor smiled a sweet smile. "That is exactly why I want to see Him," she said.

Her father threw up his hands. Though he often was impatient with his only daughter, he loved her very much. He knew that in the end he would do anything she asked of him. And Princess Eleanor knew it too.

The king called in his Chief of Law and Order.

"My daughter demands to see God," he said. "I order you to take care of it."

The Chief of Law and Order nodded and smiled. He knew very well who God was, so far as he was concerned.

14

He had no doubt that he could make the little princess see Him too.

So he led the princess to the highest tower in the palace. He showed her the great book of the land which listed all the laws the people in that kingdom must live by, and all the punishments for those who disobeyed.

Solemnly he said, "This book is as *good as God* in this kingdom."

The king's daughter pushed the great book onto the floor.

"The law is *not* God!" she said, and she stamped her foot. "I want to see *God!*"

"Bah!" said the Chief of Law and Order, and he went off to tell the king that his daughter was rude and wilful.

So the king called his Chief of the Treasury. He had charge of all the gold in the kingdom.

"My daughter demands to see God," said the king. "I order you to take care of it."

The Chief of the Treasury nodded and smiled. For he knew very well who God was, so far as he was concerned. He had no doubt that he could make the little princess see Him too.

He led the princess down to the deepest dungeon of the castle. There he took out a great key and unlocked a thick door. As the big door swung open the glitter of gold inside made the princess blink.

"There!" the treasurer said, clasping his hands under his chin. "That, my dear, is the most money you'll ever see in your whole life!"

"But I want to see God!" The princess stamped her foot. "Not just a lot of old money!"

The treasurer looked at her flushed cheeks and laid a dry hand on her forehead. Then he hurried off to the king to say that the princess must certainly be suffering from a strange kind of sickness.

Because neither of his two chiefs had been able to handle the job at all, the king decided to do it himself. He began to look around for God.

Thinking about it, it occurred to him that he didn't know what God looked like. Of course, he had never both-

16

ered to look for Him either. So he looked in the royal corners, and under the royal bed, and even down in the royal kitchen. But he couldn't find God anywhere in the palace.

At last he went out the palace gates and trudged down the road to the village. On his way he looked up into trees, and around hedges, and under rocks. He looked everywhere. But since he was not sure just exactly what it was he was looking for, he didn't find anything.

Soon he came to an old man who was planting a pear tree. The man was so old that he hardly had a breath left in his body, yet he was planting a tree. The king smiled as he sat down to rest a moment.

"Old man," he said, chuckling a little. "Do you expect to live long enough to eat the fruits of that tree?"

The old man looked up at the king, and then looked down at the deep hole he had dug.

"No," he answered, slowly. "But I expect my children will. If not them, their children will." He looked proudly at his handiwork. "Oh, it will surely be a fine tree some day," he said happily. "God willing, that is."

The king looked at him curiously. "Say old man, do you know God?"

Now the old man turned to look at him. "Of course," he said. "Don't you?"

The king stroked his royal chin. "I'm really not at all sure. But my daughter wants more than anything in the

17

world to see God. Can you show Him to her?"

The old man straightened up. He had often heard of the little princess who had never cried. He looked up the road toward the palace. Then he looked down the road to a little house close to the roadside.

"Maybe I can," he said, thoughtfully.

When the king brought the old man before the princess, she looked at him suspiciously.

"Have you ever really seen God, old man?" she asked.

The old man nodded, smiling a little.

"Then, show Him to me!" she ordered in a hard little voice, for she didn't believe he had at all.

"First, you must do something for me," the old man said.

"What do you mean?" said the princess. "What do I have to do?"

"You will only have to come with me to visit someone you don't know."

"Then will you show me God?"

The old man nodded. "If God wills it, I will."

"And if he doesn't," she scolded, "you'll be sorry!"

She followed the old man out of the palace, down the road and toward the village. But they did not go all the way. They stopped at a small, poor house close to the road.

The old man sat down on a box in the yard. "Go in," he said.

The princess looked at him in surprise. She had never been in a place so poor as this before. Timidly, she pushed open the door and stepped in.

18

A poor girl sat in a chair at the table. Though her smile was bright, her face was quite dirty.

"I am Princess Eleanor," the princess said a little haughtily, and she wrinkled her nose at the smell of something cooking on the stove.

The girl only looked at her. She did not move.

"You're supposed to get up and bow when you meet a princess!" the princess said.

The girl's smile slipped off her face. "I can't," she whispered.

"What do you mean, you can't!" the princess said, and she frowned. The closeness of the little room was beginning to make her head ache.

The girl pulled at her skirt. She pointed to her legs. "I can't walk," she whispered. "I never could walk—ever."

"Oh!" said Princess Eleanor. She looked at the girl's legs, and then looked quickly away. Hastily she stepped out and closed the door.

Silently, she followed the old man back up the road to the palace.

When they reached the palace hall, the old man turned to her.

"Are you ready?" he said.

"Ready? For what?" asked the princess. She had been so busy thinking of the other girl that she had forgotten all about herself.

The old man smiled. "You are ready," he said. To the

princess' surprise, he put a mirror in her hand.

"Now close your eyes, hold up the mirror, and look deep into your heart."

The princess closed her eyes and held up the mirror. Suddenly tears began to roll down the cheeks of the princess who had never cried. Big, soft, wet tears.

"Why are you crying?" asked the old man.

"I have been selfish all my life," she said, "and I did not know it until I saw that poor girl." She put the mirror down and opened her eyes.

"Oh sir, do you think it would help if I brought her some good soup, and maybe a pretty dress to wear? Do you think that would help?"

The old man smiled. He took the mirror from her hand and put it carefully away.

"You have seen God," he said.

III

YOU SHALL NOT SWEAR FALSELY BY THE NAME OF THE LORD YOUR GOD

III

I T WAS strange how loud the voice of God seemed to the Israelites, even though they heard Him only in their hearts. It was so loud that its echo was heard everywhere. The Israelites trembled at the words of the Third Commandment. It is said that the whole world trembled too.

Though the day was warm, and the great flames blazing from the top of the mountain seemed hot, many shivered.

Swearing falsely by the name of the Lord is doing something which hurts you forever, the commandment said. For no one will ever again believe a person who once breaks a promise to tell the truth. No one will trust him completely ever again. His name will never be "clear."

The Israelites stood very still, thinking of the meaning

22

of the Third Commandment. They thought of what it meant to each one alone, and then they could see what it meant to all of them together.

When people do not speak the truth, the world becomes a place where people cannot trust each other. A world in which people cannot trust each other becomes a world of fear. God was telling them that a person who breaks a promise to tell the truth hurts not only himself, but the whole world.

A murmur arose from the Israelites. They heard the Third Commandment, and they knew it was a rule not only for themselves, but for all men to live by.

A Place Called Kushta

ONCE THERE was a town called Kushta. The people who lived there never broke their word, nor did they ever seem to grow old.

Not many of the inhabitants knew why they never seemed to grow old. But since they were happy, and always kept their word, they had never bothered their heads much about it.

One day a king's messenger happened to lose his way and wandered into this little town. He didn't stay long, but he stayed long enough. When he returned to his own country he brought to the king a most unusual tale.

"In that place, no one ever grows old!" he said to the king.

The king's eyes gleamed. Immediately he summoned his wisest counsellor.

"In Kushta, no one ever grows old," said the king. "Find out why!"

24

Now this counsellor knew a great many things. For instance, he knew why apples fell down, and why birds fly high. He knew why the earth turned, and why the stars blinked. (Though he didn't know what would keep the king from growing old.)

"But I don't mind trying to find out!" he said, and he travelled to the town of Kushta.

He walked up and down through the streets of Kushta and looked carefully around. All about him he saw ripe golden apricots hanging from the trees. Everywhere he looked he saw people eating them. The women loaded their aprons with them, the children stuffed their mouths, and the men filled their pockets.

"Aha!" he thought. *"This* must be the reason that no one in Kushta ever grows old."

So he picked a basket full of the ripe fruit. Strapping it carefully to his saddle, he galloped his horse swiftly back to the king.

The king was very pleased when his wise counsellor returned with the beautiful apricots. "I will reward you," he said.

But instead of keeping his promise, he ordered his guards to lock up the counsellor. The king certainly didn't intend to let anyone else learn the secret of never growing old.

In his private chamber, the king sat down and began to devour the apricots greedily. He ate and he ate, and when he had eaten all there were in the basket, he went eagerly to his mirror.

But instead of making him look younger, the apricots seemed only to have made him look older, and, suddenly, much greener too! In a rage, he smashed the mirror and ordered the faithful counsellor put to death.

It wasn't long before the king sent another counsellor to Kushta to find what it was that kept the people from growing old.

Now, the second counsellor was even wiser than the first. For instance, he knew why some numbers are round, and some square. He knew why clouds made rain and why ice melted. (Though he didn't know what would keep the king from growing old.)

26

"But I don't mind trying to find out!" he said, and travelled to the town of Kushta. When he reached Kushta, he set about to find the answer to the king's question. He walked up and down the streets of the town and looked carefully around.

All about him were great barrels catching the rain. Everywhere he looked he saw people drinking the fresh water from the clouds. The women washed their hair in it; the children bathed in it; the men splashed it on their faces.

"Aha!" he thought. "This must be the reason that no one ever grows old here." Quickly he filled a barrel with the rainwater and took it back to the king.

The king was very pleased when the rainwater was brought to him. He ordered it poured into his large tiled tub, and promised to reward his counsellor immediately. But before taking his rainwater bath, he secretly ordered his guards to lock up the second counsellor, for, of course, the king intended to keep the secret for himself.

He stepped into the tub. But alas, when he arose again he was no younger, and only a little bit cleaner.

Shaking with anger, as well as with cold, the king ordered the second counsellor put to death.

"I will go myself to the place where no one ever grows old," he decided, and ordered his carriage. He travelled with great speed, and he carried with him a sack of gold.

Reaching the town of Kushta, he drove straight to the city square. Curious, all the people gathered round.

The king stepped out of the carriage. He peered carefully about him. Sure enough, no matter where he turned, he saw no person who looked old.

Holding his bag of gold high in the air, he shouted, "A handsome reward for anyone who will tell me what I want to know!"

"What do you want to know?" A young man spoke. (He might have been an old man for all the king could tell.)

The king smiled. "Tell me," he said softly, "why the people of Kushta never grow old."

The people looked at each other wide-eyed. Not many of them really knew.

But the king thought they did not trust him. He raised his right hand and said, "I am a king, and you can take my word for it. I swear to you I will reward you handsomely if you tell me your secret."

"It's no secret," one said. "This is the town of truth. That is why it is called Kushta. In our language 'Kushta' means truth. As long as we live we always tell the truth." He scratched his head. "I guess that's why we live so long," he said, as though he had not thought about it before.

Everyone nodded. One of them eagerly raised his hands for the bag of gold.

But the secret didn't sound like anything of much value to the king. He pushed the fellow back roughly.

The townsman looked surprised. "The gold!" he said. "You promised to give us a bag of gold!"

But the king was no fool. Why should he give them his

gold for nothing? He took his bag of gold and jumped into the carriage. Wildly he whipped his horses home.

But, strangely enough, when the carriage reached the palace gates, the king who had broken his word in a place called Kushta was dead.

Something even stranger began to happen in Kushta. The people who had never grown old before suddenly began to grow older.

When the king broke his promise in the town of truth, the spell (if a spell it was) was broken too. People didn't trust each other so completely any more.

And today, if a traveller should happen to stop at the town called Kushta, he would find it hardly different from any other place.

IV

REMEMBER
THE SABBATH DAY
AND
KEEP IT HOLY

IV

REMEMBER
THE SABBATH DAY
AND
KEEP IT HOLY

THE ISRAELITES looked at each other, hardly believing their ears. In the Fourth Commandment God gave them the Sabbath as a day of rest. It was to be their day as well as His forever.

They were partners with God! They were God's people, the Fourth Commandment told them. Thinking about it, the Israelites stood a little straighter and a little taller.

As free people, the commandment said, they must care about the people around them as well as themselves, and they must care for their families and their animals.

Perhaps the Fourth Commandment more than any other gave them hope and gave them courage, for it was more than a reminder, more than a warning, more than a rule. It was a promise. It was a Covenant between the Israelites

and God. It would be a sign between them forever. The Fourth Commandment was also a pattern for them to follow. It showed them how to live.

The Israelites took the Fourth Commandment most particularly to their hearts. They made it the center of their religion, and lived their lives around it.

The Sweetest Sound

ING RUBEN was always asking questions. Every Monday and Thursday he had a new question to ask.

"Where is the hottest place in the world?" he wanted to know. "Where does the snow fall the deepest?" And— "What is the best month of the year?"

One Thursday he called all his advisors together to ask, "What is the sweetest melody of all?"

His wise men rubbed their chins and looked at each other. They opened their dictionaries and their encyclopedias. They searched through their books of knowledge. Nowhere could they find the answer.

"Why don't you have a contest to find the sweetest melody?" they advised.

So the king called all the musicians in the kingdom to the palace to play their sweetest tunes.

Early in the morning they began to gather before the

king's window. They came with flutes and harps and violins, with horns and bells and drums. There were banjos and bugles and chimes and cymbals and gongs and triangles, lutes and lyres and trumpets and more.

The sounds of their tuning and scraping and testing woke the king at sunrise.

Smiling, King Ruben jumped out of his royal bed.

"Each one in turn will play a tune," he ordered. "When you have all finished, I will decide which melody is the sweetest to my ears."

So they began. All through the morning, the king sat on his balcony and listened. By noon he had listened to all the sounds imaginable that could be made by plucking, tinkling, blowing, and banging.

"What do you think?" one advisor asked.

And—"What do *you* think?" another advisor answered.

Then they cupped their hands around their ears and listened some more.

By the middle of the afternoon, the king had heard all the melodies which could be made by whistling, jingling and shaking, by sawing, buzzing and pounding.

"O king!" said the advisors. "To your ears, which melody is the sweetest?"

King Ruben listened through one ear, then he listened through the other. He listened standing up, and he listened sitting down. He listened with his eyes closed, and he even tried listening with his mouth open.

By late Friday afternoon, every sound-making instrument in the whole land had been brought before the king and made to play its sweetest tune.

"Hmm," said the king. "Hmmmm" he said again. But he could not tell exactly which sound was the sweetest.

Then the wisest advisor stepped forward. "Why don't you ask all the musicians to play their instruments at the same time? Surely when you hear them all together, the sweetest melody will be easy to find."

The king clapped his hands. "Wonderful!" he said. And he gave the signal for all the instruments in the kingdom to be played at the same time.

The violins sang, the flutes burbled, the harps twanged, the horns blew, the bells rang, the drums pounded, the banjos bonged, the bugles blared, the chimes pealed, the cymbals banged, the gongs rang, the triangles jingled, the lyres strummed, the trumpets blared, the pipes whistled, the lutes lilted, and all the other instruments rattled and beat and gurgled as sweetly as they could. All together! At the same time!

King Ruben wrinkled up his face and listened with all his might. The advisors covered their ears with their hands and raised their eyes to heaven.

Just at this moment, a woman dressed in her Sabbath best pushed her way to the front of the crowd.

"Oh king, sir!" she called at the top of her voice.

The noise was so great the king could hardly hear her.

36

He leaned over and put his ear close to her mouth.

"I have the answer to your question!" she shouted.

"Eh?" said King Ruben.

"The answer!" she said. "I have it!"

The king looked at her with surprise. She carried no instrument at all.

"Why didn't you come up before!" he shouted above all the tunes. And he clasped his hands to his head, for it was beginning to ache.

The woman said, "If you please sir, I had to wait until the sun was about to set."

The king looked at the musicians puffing and blowing and pounding and strumming. Sure enough, the sun was low. But there was so much noise he could no longer hear himself think.

"Stop!" he shouted to all the music makers.

"Stop! Stop!" shouted the advisors.

And just as the sun dipped to the horizon, the sounds of the farthest instruments began to fade away.

"Well?" said King Ruben.

The woman took two candles from her pocket. She placed them on the railing of the balcony. She struck a match. The flames of the candles flickered up just as the sun began to go down. Covering her eyes with her hands, she said.

"Blessed art thou O Lord our God, King of the Universe, Who sanctified us by Thy commandments and commanded us to kindle the Sabbath lights."

Then she took her hands away from her face. "He that has ears to hear, let him hear," she said.

The king raised his head. The advisors took their hands away from their ears. The people in the crowd put down their instruments.

"What is it?" whispered the king. He could hear nothing at all.

"It is the sound of rest," the woman said. "Listen, my king, and tell me—is not the peace of the Sabbath the sweetest melody of all to men?"

The king listened; the wise men listened; the people listened. The sound of rest filled the kingdom. At the blessed quiet, King Ruben breathed a sigh of relief.

"Ahhhhhhhhhh," he said.

"Ahhhhhhhhhh," echoed all the people.

Then—"Ah!" said the king again. For he had his answer.

"The peace of the Sabbath to the ears of men is the sweetest melody of all!"

V

HONOR
YOUR FATHER
AND
YOUR MOTHER

V

HONOR YOUR FATHER AND YOUR MOTHER

THE VOICE of Moses grew loud and stern as he read the words of the Fifth Commandment. The words seemed to shine on the tablets of stone.

"Honor is love, honor is respect," the older children explained to the younger ones.

Then even the smallest child knew how important this commandment was. Their parents had told them they must honor God. Now God was telling them to love and respect their parents. It was exactly the same!

Children and parents smiled at each other. Showing that you honor your parents was part of the way you honor God. They all understood it.

The Israelites listened to the Fifth Commandment and remembered Abraham. God had promised Abraham that his people, the Israelites, would be a great nation. But at the same time he had given a warning. "A nation without honor for God will not endure!"

As a nation, they were only beginning. In the Fifth Commandment God was telling them how to make sure that they would become a great nation that would go on forever.

Thoughtfully they looked again at the glowing words on the tablets of stone. Honor was like a great mirror. Wherever it was held it reflected back again.

The Israelites nodded. Now they knew exactly what those words meant.

A Big Red Tomato

HURRYING a little, Mr. Benjamin closed up his grocery store. He could hardly wait to get home. Something very special had happened that day.

But before he went out the door, he picked up the biggest, roundest, most beautiful tomato he could find in the window. Mr. Benjamin smiled as he thought how pleased his mother would be with such a fine tomato.

On his way home, he stopped to see his parents and to leave the tomato, though he did not tell them what had happened. There's no fun in spoiling a surprise, Mr. Benjamin believed.

He couldn't help grinning as he drove his car into his garage.

"Margaret!" he called to his wife, even before he had opened the kitchen door. "Margaret! It's happened!"

"What's happened?" said Mrs. Benjamin, but she didn't

really have to ask. Somehow she already knew, and she began to smile.

Mr. and Mrs. Benjamin had no children. For a long time they had looked for a baby to adopt. They had written letters, and filled out application forms, and taken health tests—and waited. They had waited and waited.

Mr. Benjamin pulled a letter from his pocket. "It has finally come!" he said.

His wife read it. She looked at him doubtfully. "But it doesn't say they have a baby for us. It only says that they want to talk to you."

Mr. Benjamin looked at the letter again. She was right. That was all it said. But he smiled anyway.

"Oh, that's just the way it's written," he said. "What they mean is they have a baby for us—if we want it."

"Of course we want it!" said Mrs. Benjamin.

"We'll get it all right!" Mr. Benjamin said.

But he wasn't quite so sure when he arrived at the adoption office the next day.

"So you want to be a father," Mr. Day said. He looked at the letter Mr. Benjamin showed him.

Mr. Benjamin nodded.

Mr. Day sat down behind his desk. He pressed a button. It made a buzzing sound. The office door opened and a young woman came in.

"The other prospective father is waiting outside," she said.

"You mean there are two babies?" Mr. Benjamin asked.

Mr. Day shook his head. "No, there is only one baby who needs a home. But there are two families who want him."

Feeling uneasy, Mr. Benjamin stood aside as the other man came in. He looks something like me, he thought. It was true. As they stood side by side before the desk, they were much alike. They were about the same age, with the same color hair. They both wore the same sort of suit— and they were both nervous. I guess he's just as anxious as I am, Mr. Benjamin thought.

"I have called you here for a very important reason," Mr. Day said to them. "I read your applications carefully. They were almost complete—but not quite." Mr. Benjamin wondered what he had left out.

"There is something neither of you mentioned. Something so important that it is of more account than all the fine things either of you have promised to give this child."

Mr. Benjamin looked at him in surprise.

But suddenly Mr. Day began to talk of something else. "You have parents living nearby?" he asked politely.

The other man answered quickly. "Oh yes!" he said. "And wouldn't they just love a grandchild! Why they'd be tickled pink to have a little one to come visit."

"I guess you don't see them much then," Mr. Day asked without much interest.

"Oh, we see them all right. Birthdays and that sort of thing. I've always made it a special point to do my duty. You know—honor your father and mother and all that," he said grandly. "I always send them something pretty fancy for their anniversary. Something really expensive!"

"And when is the last time you saw them?" Mr. Day asked, as if it wasn't very important.

The other man took time to think. "Along about New Year's last, I guess. Oh no—we were pretty busy then. I guess it was before that."

A tight knot was growing bigger and bigger in Mr. Benjamin's chest. If the choice was going to be made on how big a gift he had given his parents—well, he guessed he was out.

"And when did you last see your parents?" Mr. Day asked him.

Mr. Benjamin raised his head. "Yesterday," he mumbled. "I stopped by to give my mother a big red tomato." It sounded odd, he knew. He added quickly, "She loves tomatoes, and it was a specially nice one and . . ." his voice trailed off.

He guessed it was all over for him. A tomato didn't sound like much. It didn't sound like anything at all. He raised his head and met Mr. Day's gaze.

"It's just that she specially likes tomatoes," he said. Then he didn't know what more to say.

Mr. Day stood up. "What neither of you mentioned in your written application is what you would give this child besides his food and clothing and other things. We think that's important. Very important."

The man who looked like Mr. Benjamin scratched his head. "How do you mean?" he asked.

"The love a father will give his child can be judged by the honor the father shows to his own parents," Mr. Day said carefully.

"I gave them a television set!" the other man said quickly.

Mr. Day nodded. He turned to Mr. Benjamin. He said kindly, "Mr. Benjamin would you mind waiting in the other room a moment?"

Slowly Mr. Benjamin went into the other room. He sat there staring at the floor. He didn't know what he was going to tell Margaret.

"A television set," he mumbled, as Mr. Day came in.

Mr. Day nodded. "A good dutiful gift," he said. "Even generous. But how can it compare with a gift of love?" He stood there smiling at Mr. Benjamin.

Mr. Benjamin's mouth fell open. "A big red tomato?" he said, not sure he was hearing right.

Mr. Day said, "A gift of honor!"

Mr. Benjamin began to smile, too.

"A man who honors his parents is sure to be a good father to his own child," Mr. Day said softly.

But Mr. Benjamin hardly heard him. He was thinking of what he had to tell Margaret, and his grin stretched all the way around his face.

VI

YOU
SHALL NOT
MURDER

VI

YOU
SHALL NOT
MURDER

EVERYBODY was
quiet. Everybody was still. They listened to the Sixth Commandment. Clearly it did not mean that people shouldn't
kill chickens and cows and other animals to eat, because
people have to eat to live. The commandment was against
killing without need. That was murder.

Then everybody began to move together and to speak
to one another. For they understood that the Sixth Commandment was not about death. It was about life.

Life was what made them breathe. It made their hearts
beat. It made them feel and think. But no one could
really say exactly *what* it was.

"Life is good," one Israelite said softly.

They remembered they had been told how God made

the world and called it good. And how He had given life to man, and called this very good.

"Life is good!" The Israelites repeated, one after another.

And then they began to understand what the Sixth Commandment was telling them. It meant "life is good." It is good above everything else. That is why you must value it.

You must protect life and treasure it, appreciate it and make the most of it. Not only your own life, the commandment said, but the lives of all others. For every life is a world, God was saying, like His world.

The Israelites breathed deeply, feeling the breath of life in their bodies. Life was good. They smiled, thinking that now they knew what the Sixth Commandment meant.

Then they heard a sound of thunder. It boomed like a warning over their heads.

It reminded them that the Sixth Commandment said something more. It said no one must take away in anger the life which God had given in love. No one must murder.

His Name was Hyam

ONE DAY a stranger came riding his horse into a little town. Tied to his belt was a bag. It clinked with gold pieces when he jumped off his horse.

"Good afternoon, stranger!" called a townsman. "Where are you headed for?"

The stranger didn't bother to answer. He had a few questions to ask himself.

"Who is the bravest fellow hereabouts?" he asked the tavern keeper.

"Who has more ambition than he has gold?" he asked the barber.

"Who can keep a silent tongue in his head, when necessary, yet talk himself into good favor?" he asked the baker.

It was a very small village, and everywhere he went the answer was the same.

"Hyam," they said. "It's Hyam you're looking for. He's

50

a hard worker. He'll do almost anything for a dollar. He has one eye on the prettiest girl in the village, and the other on a piece of the finest land hereabouts. He sings with the best of them in the evening. But he's up before the sun every morning to say his prayers. He's a good lad. that Hyam."

The stranger frowned. "A *good* lad?"

"And ambitious," said the barber. "He's the most ambitious boy around here."

The stranger smiled. "Tell me," he said, "where can I find him?"

"Who knows?" said the tavern keeper. "One day he is here, one day he is there! He is not one to stay in the same place very long. Not when there is work to be done!"

"And where is here, and where is there?" the stranger asked. He seemed much pleased.

"*Here* is the little synagogue on the corner, where he dusts the altar and sweeps the school rooms. And *there* is the little farmhouse on the other side of the river."

The tavern keeper came out to shout after the traveller. "Watch the little bridge," he called. "It's a shaky one!"

The stranger nodded, and rode through the village. The bridge was a very shaky one. To cross it he slid off his horse and walked over, leading the horse behind him. The tiny bridge went across a deep river. Great rocks choked the river, and the water swirled around them. The stranger shivered and held tightly to the railing.

51

Soon he reached the little farmhouse. He looked at it with interest. It was neat and stout and well-kept, but to his mind there wasn't much there worth keeping. He smiled contentedly to himself as he tied his horse to the fence post and rapped at the door.

"Who is there?" was the answer.

The stranger did not bother to answer. He knocked again.

The door was flung open, and standing in the doorway was a young man so tall, so strong, and with eyes so clear and blue, that the stranger stepped back in surprise.

"Hyam?" he asked. "You are Hyam?"

"I am Hyam," was the answer. "Who are you?"

The stranger only smiled. "It is better you do not know my name if you are the one I'm looking for."

Hyam looked curiously at the stranger. "All right, Mr. No-name," he said. "Come in." When the stranger had sat down, Hyam said, "Tell me, why do you think I am the man you are looking for?"

The stranger looked around the poor room. Everything was neat and everything was clean, but luxurious it was not.

"Because I have what you want," he replied.

"And what is it I want?" asked Hyam.

"That is easy to see. You want a beautiful girl for a wife. And you want that fine rich land I rode through for a farm. You want a fine house to put your wife into, and more land to build it on."

52

Hyam laughed. "Are you a fortune-teller?" he asked. "One of those fellows who travels around promising *little for much?*"

The stranger laughed, too. "I am not a fortune-teller," he said, "but it is about a fortune I have come to see you."

"Mine?" said the young man, making a joke.

"Yours," said the stranger. "If you want it, that is."

Hyam looked at him. "Who should not want a fortune, sir?" he said lightly, but his eyes began to gleam.

The stranger drew his chair close. "I have with me a bag of gold," he said. "It will be yours if you do something for me."

Hyam leaned forward eagerly. "What is that?"

"Kill a man."

Hyam rose. His chair fell back onto the floor. Suddenly he laughed. "It's a joke!" he said. "A fine joke, sir! Now tell me what you came for and let me get on with my work."

But the stranger did not laugh with him. "It is no joke," he said.

Hyam stared at his visitor. The laughter went out of his face. "I cannot kill a man," he said. "Not for all the gold in the world. I cannot kill anyone. Not a dog in the street, or even the ant that fell into my soup last night."

The visitor looked at him impatiently. "Come, come," he said. "You are an ambitious lad. I know that. And it is a simple enough thing to do." He pushed the sack of gold toward him.

54

Hyam opened the door. He picked up the sack of gold and threw it out the doorway. "Goodby," he said. "You are only a fortune-teller after all. You want a lot for a little. All the gold in the world is not worth as much as one life." Then he grinned at his visitor, "If you don't believe me, just ask the man whose life it is!"

"Bah!" said the stranger. He picked up his sack of gold. Mounting his horse, he pulled angrily at the reins. The horse reared up, turned around, and broke into a fast gallop.

"The bridge is shaky!" shouted Hyam, and closed the door.

About an hour later he heard a strange noise in the yard. Opening the door, he saw the traveller's horse running around wildly, riderless.

"The bridge!" thought Hyam. He jumped on his own horse and flew to the shaky bridge. It was still standing, but a rail had broken away. Looking below, Hyam saw his recent visitor clinging to a rock. Hyam threw off his coat and jumped into the wild water.

"It is too late," shouted the desperate man.

But Hyam paid no attention. He tried again and again to reach the man. And again and again he was thrown back by the surge of the river.

"I'm afraid you can't," gasped the stranger, and his hands began to slip from the rock.

"I can!" shouted Hyam. "I will!"

Slowly he dragged the man up to the bank.

"Are you all right?" Hyam asked, when he could breathe again.

"Yes," was the answer. "Yes, I am all right." He turned to stare at Hyam.

"There's one thing I don't understand," he said. "A little while ago you refused a fortune in gold because a life was too valuable. Yet now you almost threw your own life away for nothing."

Hyam took a deep breath. "True," he said. "And I'll tell you why. When God created man, He just the same as created a whole new world. Every life is like a world, you see. Me, murder?" He shook his head. "If I destroyed one person, it would be the same to God as if I had destroyed the whole world."

"But you almost destroyed your own life to save mine!" said the stranger. He still couldn't understand.

Hyam smiled. "The way God counts—saving a life is the same as saving a whole world, too!"

With a grin, the boy named Hyam climbed on his horse and whistled his way home.

VII

YOU
SHALL NOT
COMMIT ADULTERY

VII

WHEN THE Israelites heard these words, husbands and wives stepped close to each other. For in the Seventh Commandment, God was blessing their marriage.

He was reminding them that marriage is holy. He was telling them that two people who are married to each other are promised to each other. Husbands and wives among the Israelites nodded in understanding.

They remembered how God had made Adam first, then Eve.

When Adam slept, God took one of his ribs and made it into a woman. When Adam awoke, and saw the woman, God said, "You belong together."

"Of course!" Adam and Eve said, because they were part

of each other. God had married them to each other.

A marriage tells the whole world that one man and one woman have made a promise to each other, and they belong together.

As they listened to the words of the Seventh Commandment, many of the Israelites were thinking of how in marriage both troubles and joys were shared. Sharing pain, each suffered only half as much. But sharing joy, their happiness doubled.

But there were many who heard in God's words a stern warning. He was saying that marriage makes a man and a woman one in His eyes, and nobody must do anything to separate them or keep them apart.

The Rabbi's Eye

T O A TOWN long ago, there came a great Rabbi. He came with a fine sermon, and a silken prayer shawl, and a head full of learning.

Now in this town lived a very wise man and his very wise wife. But the wisdom of the husband was different from the wisdom of the wife.

The husband was known for making up his mind about everything very quickly. He was also known for never changing his mind. Ah, thought the people of this little town, a man indeed was very wise who never ever changed his mind about anything.

On the other hand, his wife was wise in another way. She had a good ear for listening. It was said of this good wife that she could listen patiently to any person, be he wise man or fool, with nothing in her face to show that there was a difference between them. A woman was indeed wise who treated a fool as if he were a wise man, thought the people of this little town.

It was truly a perfect marriage, the town agreed. And which was the wiser of the two, no one could agree. Some said it was the wife, and some said it was the husband. But so long as they were happy together, it was decided, it really made no difference.

As the story goes, even before the great Rabbi arrived the wise husband made it known that he didn't think the Rabbi such a wise one at all. And since he never changed his mind about anything, that is what he continued to think. Not even his wife could change his mind.

She had gone straight off to listen to the great Rabbi. And she had listened, as usual, very wisely.

"He is a great man!" she came rushing home to tell her husband. "He is a wonderful Rabbi!"

Her husband stood in the doorway of their house, glowering at her.

"While you sat listening to the Rabbi, our dinner burned!" he said.

"Oh dear!" said the wise wife. "What shall I do?"

"You can go back to that so-called great Rabbi," said the angry husband, "and you can spit in his eye!"

The woman's chin dropped in surprise. "I will not!" she said. "I certainly will not!"

"You will," said the husband who never changed his mind. "You will, or you won't enter this house tonight!" And the wise husband who made up his mind very fast and never changed it, went inside and closed the door behind him.

Since the wise wife would not insult the great Rabbi in any such way, she stayed out in the street. Finally a kind neighbor opened her door and called to her to come in.

There she stayed awhile. But her husband would not change his mind.

All the people in the neighborhood came to her offering advice. She listened to each one. But she was such a wise woman, no one knew whether she really heard what they had said.

It was not long before the story was carried to the ears of the great Rabbi himself.

Now the great Rabbi was a very understanding man. He was very simple and very kind, too. At once he called for the woman to come to see him. So she patted her hair and arranged her face in its wisest listening expression, and she went.

Strangely, the great Rabbi didn't seem to have much to say to her. He invited her into the garden. He showed her a new rose. And he talked. He talked about this, and he talked about that. But he didn't really *say* anything at all.

The wise woman smiled and nodded as if his unimportant talk was great wisdom indeed.

Then—"Oh!" he said suddenly.

"What's the matter?" she asked.

The Rabbi stood there, his hand over his eye.

"A speck!" he said. "A speck flew into my eye."

"Oh, what shall I do?" asked the good woman. A speck in the eye can be a very serious thing, she knew.

"I know of an old-fashioned remedy," he said. "Please— if you don't mind—spit in my eye. Spit in my eye seven times," he said.

And as the woman hesitated, he groaned.

"Ohhhhh!" he said. "How it hurts!"

Quickly she did as the Rabbi told her. She spit in his eye seven times. Then she gave him a clean white handkerchief. She looked anxiously at him.

The Rabbi smiled. He took the handkerchief away from his eye. So well had the remedy worked that the eye wasn't even red.

"It's all right. Everything is all right now. Everything!" he said, smiling and nodding as he bid her goodby.

The wise woman walked slowly home. And when she got to her house, she smiled. She ran up to her door and flung it open.

"I have spit in his eye!" she cried. "Just as you told me to!" And that was all she said.

The wise husband kissed his wise wife. They settled down and lived as happily as before. But the people of the town never got done with talking of it.

"It proves that the husband was the wisest," said one. "Because he didn't have to change his mind."

"No," said another. "It proves that the wife was the wisest. For she didn't talk too much, which shows her a very wise woman indeed."

But there was one old man who said that the wisest of all was none other than the Rabbi. For it was he who made peace between a man and his wife. And it was he who turned an insult into a good deed.

And there were many who thought that the old man was right. Do you?

YOU
SHALL NOT
STEAL

VIII

YOU SHALL NOT STEAL

Y OU SHALL not steal."
How simple the Eighth Commandment sounded.

"Go on," some of the Israelites said to Moses. They didn't think this commandment said anything more. But Moses didn't go on to the next commandment. He waited until the little words had been heard deeply in all their hearts.

Taking something that belonged to someone else was stealing. Everyone knew that. When you stole something you were punished. A slave who took what was not his was whipped by his master.

Thinking of that, the Israelites felt something strange and new. They had been thinking of themselves as slaves.

66

A slave is responsible to his master. But the Israelites were their own masters now. They were free people.

"Free!" someone called out, thinking aloud.

As they thought about it, they could see that a free man had even greater burdens than a slave. For a free man must be responsible to himself for whatever he does. He must be his own master. He must tell himself what to do. When he does what is right, he pleases himself, and that is the way he pleases God.

The Eighth Commandment really meant that free men must respect one another and respect what belongs to others.

"YOU SHALL NOT STEAL." It was strange how big the words sounded when the meaning became clear.

The Reward

ONCE THERE was a very clever young man who owned nothing but the clothes on his back and the smile on his face.

One day, in the court of King Solomon, he met an old artist who was looking for an apprentice.

"I need someone to learn my craft," the old man said. "If you promise to work hard I will teach you all I know."

The young man shrugged. "Why not?" he said. But he had no intention of working very hard. His head was full of plans to earn money doing no work at all.

Luckily for him, the old man was so honest and so busy that it did not occur to him that his clever young apprentice was paying no attention to the careful instructions he gave him.

News of the old painter's young apprentice soon reached the ears of the king. Now, he was a very wise king and a very kind one, too. He was pleased to hear that his old friend had found someone who would help him with the work he loved.

He called the two before him. "You must each paint my portrait," he said. And with a nod to the apprentice, he added, "Each one exactly like the other." For the king knew that young people learn by copying their elders.

The old artist smiled. Never had the king had a portrait made of himself. To be chosen to do so was a great honor. And what a splendid opportunity for his young apprentice, he thought.

"I will do my best, O king," he said, and he meant it.

But the young man, who was very clever, saw a way to become rich with no work at all. He said, "But my king! A portrait to do you honor should be painted in gold and silver, with rubies and sapphires!" He shrugged his shoulders sadly. "We are but poor craftsmen. Where would we get such magnificent materials?"

"I do not expect you to make a king's likeness out of ordinary materials," the king said. "Whatever you need you shall have, both of you. Now go and get ready, and come back tomorrow. I will sit every afternoon for you until the portrait is finished."

The clever young man said quickly, "But you must not ask to see the portraits until they are completed."

To the old artist his words seemed exceedingly wise.

"Agreed!" said the king.

So every day the king sat for his portrait. Every day

the old artist worked with eager eyes and hands. And every day the clever young man went through the motions, as if he too were painting the king's portrait. But his canvas was blank, and he thought only of the rubies and pearls and diamonds that lay before him.

Pretending to measure the paint, he measured instead fine gold-dust enough to fill the pockets of his shirt. He dropped a ruby under his tongue when he licked his paint-brush to a fine point, and every afternoon he walked away from the palace with a pearl in the toe of his shoe. After the old man had fallen asleep, he spent his nights lining his clothes with secret pockets. He carried his treasure with him wherever he went.

Each day the portrait came closer to being finished, and each day the canvas upon which the young man worked remained blank.

The young man planned carefully. He would stay, stealing all he could, until the last day but one, and on that day he would disappear. Poof! Just like that.

Unfortunately for him, it did not happen just like that. One day—three days too early—the old artist laid down his brush and said joyfully, "It is done!"

The young man looked up in surprise. Quickly he hid his blank canvas under a cover of velvet.

"You are finished, too, of course!" the king said. He rose and stretched.

"Of course!" the young man said, thinking fast. But of course he wasn't.

"Now I have a surprise for you," the king said. He clapped his hands.

Into the room came two of the king's servants. They carried two golden tubs, and two large bars of sweet-smelling soap, and two great soft towels. Behind them came

71

more servants with underclothes of silk, and trousers of velvet, and shirts of finest satin.

"You will be my guests at dinner," the king announced. "And after dinner, I will view the finished portraits!"

The old artist looked at the warm water in the tubs and at the fine clothes. He smiled with pleasure.

The young man frowned. In his secret pockets a fortune was hidden. He hesitated a moment too long, however, for two husky young men quickly stripped him of his work clothes, rolled them into a ball, jewels and all, and carried them off.

The young apprentice sat in the tub and frowned at the water. What was he to do? He stared at the blue water around him. He studied his face reflected there and a clever plan came to him. Suddenly, he saw how he could deceive the king and save himself.

He allowed himself to be dressed in the fine clothes. When he was ready, he bowed to the king and asked him one small favor.

"O king," he said, "may I hang the portraits with my own hands? Only then will I know they are properly ready for the eyes of the king."

The king was much pleased. "As soon as our feast is over," he said, "you may take the portraits yourself into my chambers and hang them as you think they should be hung."

The clever young man smiled brightly. Directly after dinner he did as he had planned. He took two gold frames

and placed in one the portrait of the king which the old
artist had so lovingly painted. But in the other he fitted
only a mirror which he had taken from an empty room.

With much skill he placed the likeness of the king high
on one side of the king's chamber. Opposite it he hung the
framed mirror. He hung it in such a way that it reflected

exactly the portrait of the king painted by the old artist. Anyone looking would see two portraits exactly the same, down to the last detail. He chuckled to himself.

When the king arrived, he walked first to the real portrait, and he raised his head to study it. "Magnificent!" he cried. "This is truly a work of art!"

The old workman smiled with pride.

Then the king turned and raised his eyes to the portrait which was really a mirror on the opposite wall. He looked at it closely. "Amazing!" he said.

The clever young man almost laughed out loud. Truly, the mirror on the wall seemed to be a portrait of equal beauty.

The king led the two artists to his treasure room.

"I thank you," he said to the old man, and placed before him a large bag of gold.

The old artist's eyes were wide with astonishment. He had never seen so much gold.

The young man could hardly wait his turn. He congratulated himself on his cleverness and stepped up as the king placed another large bag of gold upon the table.

"Wait!" the king commanded.

Startled, the clever man stepped back.

Next to the bag of gold, the very wise king placed a mirror. "This is your reward," the king said, pointing to the reflection of the gold in the mirror.

And that is all it was.

IX

YOU SHALL NOT BEAR FALSE WITNESS AGAINST YOUR NEIGHBOR

IX

T THE WORDS of
the Ninth Commandment, women looked at each other. For
talking about each other unkindly was what some of them
had done many times.

Others heard the Ninth Commandment and felt puzzled.
Bearing false witness meant saying things which might not
be true. But it didn't seem as if just talk could hurt people
much.

"When a person tells lies about his neighbor, he is stealing," an old man said wisely. "He is stealing his neighbor's
good name."

Many looked at him in surprise. They had not thought
of it this way at all.

They began to remember how their people had become

76

slaves in Egypt. The Israelites had lived happily in Egypt for many years until a cruel Pharoah became ruler. He did not like the strangers in his land. He thought there were already too many of them. He whispered to his people— "The Israelites are enemies. They must be kept down!"

"Oh!" said the women who had looked at each other. For they remembered how these false words had helped to make it easy for the Pharoah to turn his people against the Israelites and make slaves of them.

With eyes wide open, the people who had found freedom looked at the Ninth Commandment. In it, God was telling the Israelites that all people must beware of the words they speak about others, for words could hurt like weapons.

All of them began to shake their heads in agreement, and some shouted, "We hear!"

The Gossip

ONCE THERE was a woman who talked so much about her neighbors that they all went to the Rabbi to complain.

"She tells everyone that I eat cake instead of bread!" complained one woman whose pudgy face was pink with distress. "I only said I'd like to, I didn't say I did. But she goes around telling everybody I do!"

"She says I'm too stingy to take a deep breath," said another.

"Every time she sees me she tells me how nice I look. But to everyone else she says I look terrible for my age!"

And another complained—"She's always telling people what a good cook I am. She tells everybody that I am so good that I can make poor butter taste like manna!"

"Is that bad?" said the rabbi. It seemed to him like a very good thing to be able to do.

"But she makes everybody think that I buy only the

poorest quality ingredients for my fine baking. And it is not true. I buy only the best!"

"I see," said the Rabbi. "Yes, I see."

And after he had heard all the complaints he sent for the woman to come to see him.

"Why do you make up stories about your neighbors?" he asked her.

She laughed, a pleased little laugh. "I don't really make up stories," she said. "I just tell them a little bigger than they really are."

"You see nothing wrong in that?" the Rabbi asked.

She shrugged. "Most of the time it's just the plain truth —dressed up a little."

"And the other times?"

The woman laughed nervously at the Rabbi's simple question.

"Well, the other times, it's almost the truth," she admitted.

The Rabbi frowned.

"Anyway," she explained, "It's only talk."

Thoughtfully the Rabbi looked at her. "Perhaps you are right," he said, agreeably enough.

The gossip smiled.

"After all, Rabbi," she said, "What's talk! It isn't as if I can't take back what I say."

The Rabbi only nodded. He folded his arms and talked of other things.

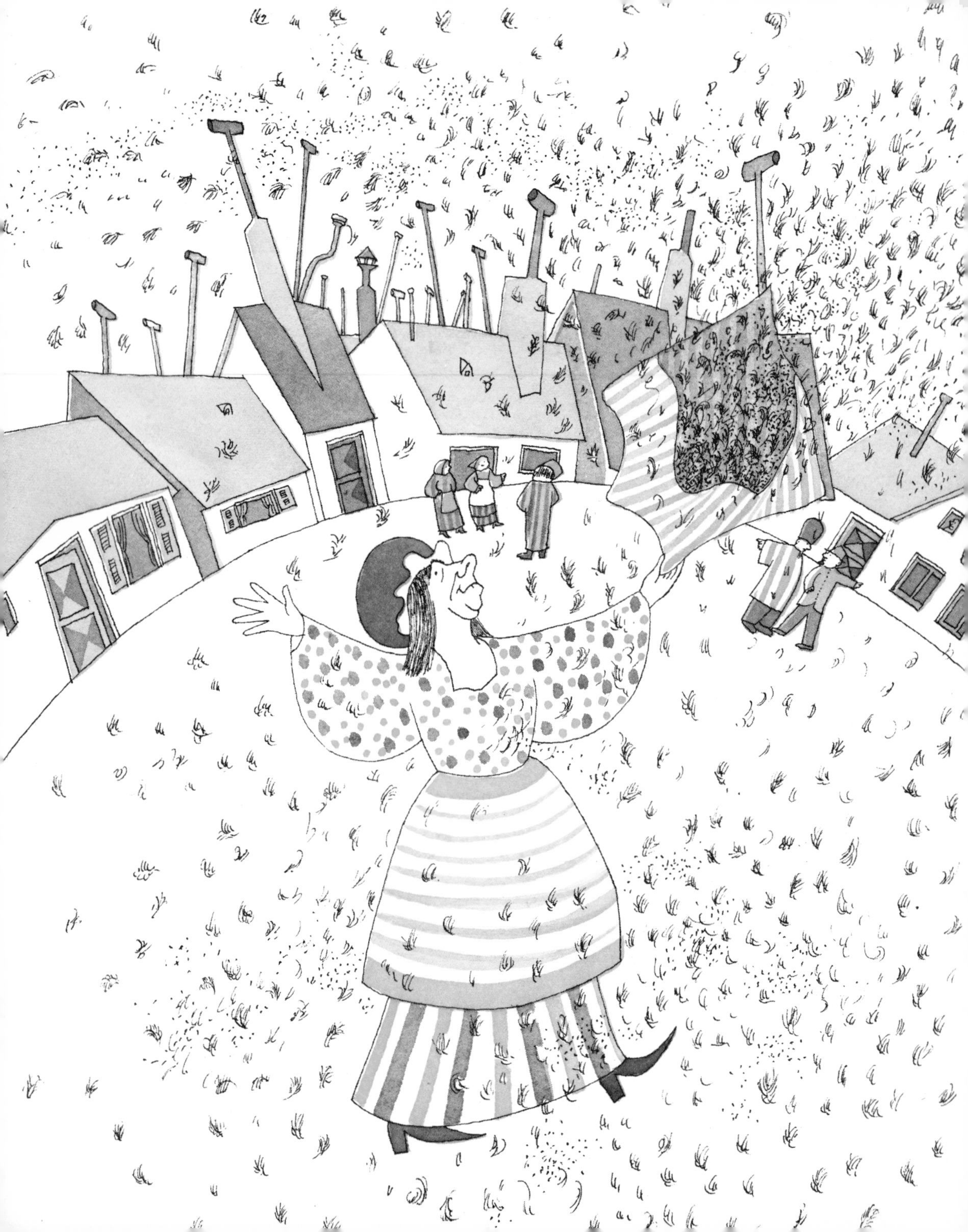

As the woman was about to leave, he asked, "I wonder if you would do something for me?"

"Of course," she said quickly. She leaned toward him. "I'm really not a mean person, Rabbi. I'll be glad to do anything I can for you."

He arose, went over to the couch in the corner and picked up a plump pillow. Handing it to her, he said, "Take this pillow to the town square."

A little surprised, she tucked it under her arm. It was fine and full, packed tight with soft feathers.

"When you get to the town square, I want you to cut it open, and shake out the feathers," the Rabbi told her.

"Cut it open!" she said. "You mean—cut it open?"

The Rabbi nodded. "Please do this for me," he said, "and afterwards return· here."

The woman shrugged. It occurred to her that perhaps their Rabbi was getting a little old. But she carried the pillow, as he asked her, to the center of the town. As she walked, she smiled to herself. Tomorrow she would have a delicious story to tell the butcher. She would say that perhaps their Rabbi could bear watching. That there were queer things going on in his head. Perhaps he was getting a little foolish. That's what she would say. She smiled, thinking of the stir she would make with her words.

Soon she reached the town square. There she did just what the Rabbi had asked her. She cut the pillow open and let the feathers fly. The light breeze in the town square blew her hat off and floated the feathers up and away. She ran after her hat and plopped it back on her head again. She could hardly wait to get home to tell her neighbors about this silly thing the Rabbi had asked her to do.

When she returned to the Rabbi's house she told him that she had done exactly as he had asked.

"Fine!" said the Rabbi.

"Oh it made quite a show!" she said gaily. "The wind picked them up and blew them all away!"

The Rabbi nodded. He seemed well pleased. He handed her a basket. "And now," he said, "If you will please go back to the square and gather them all up again."

The woman gasped. "But that is impossible!" she said.

"Ah!" said the Rabbi. "So it is impossible for you to take back all the unkind things you have said about others."

And gently he closed the door.

X

YOU SHALL NOT COVET
YOUR NEIGHBOR'S HOUSE;
YOU SHALL NOT COVET
YOUR NEIGHBOR'S WIFE,
OR HIS SERVANT,
OR ANYTHING
THAT IS YOUR NEIGHBOR'S

X

YOU SHALL NOT COVET

THE ISRAELITES gazed at the words of the last commandment.

In the other commandments, the Israelites had been told what they must not forget, what they must not do, and what they must not say. In the Tenth Commandment, they learned what they must not want.

They must not want the things which already belonged to someone else and which they could not honestly get for themselves, the Tenth Commandment said.

No matter how much they felt the want, they must not let it turn into greed. Greed is a feeling that keeps a person from seeing and keeps him from thinking until he cannot tell the difference between what is right and what is wrong.

In the Tenth Commandment God was reminding them

that man must think as well as feel. "Do not let your feelings do all your thinking for you," God was saying in this commandment.

Suddenly the Israelites understood something they had not understood before.

If they did not covet, they would not steal, they would not murder and they would not commit adultery.

God had separated a person's deeds, thoughts, words and feelings into parts by His commandments. The commandments showed how to put them together in the right way. Every commandment was part of every other commandment. All belonged together.

With a great sigh, the Israelites took the Tenth Commandment into their hearts. At last they knew how free men must live.

The Peach, the Pitcher and the Fur Coat

O NCE THERE was an old man who lived in a great house. Though he was not rich, he had three prized possessions—a peach tree, a silver pitcher, and a coat with a fur lining.

Every day he would sit at the window of his house and look at the tree growing in his yard. Only one peach grew on it.

In the house across the yard lived a woman with her son. This boy, too, spent his days at his window. His head was most often bent over his desk. But as summer wore on, it seemed to the old man that the student was gazing out the window more often than he was looking at his books.

One day, to his surprise, he did not see the face at the window. But as the days went by, he soon forgot about the boy. The peach grew ripe. It was time to pick it.

As he stood below the tree, admiring the fruit, the lady from next door called to him.

"Good sir," she said. "Have you a moment?"

"Of course," he said. "I was just about to pick my peach and eat it."

"Thank goodness!" the woman said. "Dear sir, I have a son who is sick—all because of you."

"Me?" said the old man. "How me?"

"Well, not you, exactly," she said. "I mean because of that peach you are about to eat. You see, my son sits at the window overlooking your tree. Now his yearning for that peach has made him ill."

"You don't say!" said the old man in surprise. "Well, tell him to get up out of bed, for I will be happy to give it to him!"

"Oh, thank you!" the woman said.

So the old man picked his beautiful peach and gave it away.

The weeks went by and summer turned to fall. Each day the old man sat at his window looking out upon his yard. And each day the boy sat at his desk with his eyes on his books.

As the days became colder, the old man fixed himself a bit of cocoa in the silver pitcher. Then he would sit and sip the hot cocoa and stare out at the bare garden.

He began to notice that the young man across the way was looking more at the silver pitcher than at the books before him. Shortly after that, he no longer could see the boy's head in the window. "That's funny," he thought. And as day followed day, he almost forgot about his neighbor. Then one day his front door bell rang.

"Good day!" he said warmly as he opened the door. It was the woman from next door.

"Oh dear," she said. "Oh dear, oh dear. It is not a good day at all. It is a very bad day at my house."

"What is the trouble?" the old man said.

"It is my son again, sir. He's taken to his bed, though I can't say what the trouble is. He keeps talking about a silver pitcher." She looked at the silver pitcher on the table.

"It is really of no great value," the old man said. "But I've had it for such a long time. I hardly think . . ."

The woman wrung her hands. "He is so young, my dear sir. And the young have so far to go."

"True," said the old man, but he frowned.

She said timidly, "He says, if only he could touch the beautiful silver pitcher and pretend it was his own, he would be able to get up and go on with his work."

The old man went over to his table and picked up the silver pot.

"He shall have it," he said generously. "And not just for a day. For always. You tell him it is a gift from me."

When the woman had carried his precious silver pitcher away, he stood in the middle of his room and he sighed. The young have so much to learn, he thought, and he put away his disappointment.

Every day, as usual, he sat in his window looking out. But he no longer had the peach to look upon, nor even the taste of the peach to remember. And he no longer had the silver pitcher to shine warmly at his elbow.

Nevertheless he was content with what he did have. There was his fur-lined robe, which he laid about his shoulders every day. It pleased him to see the student's head so earnestly bent over his books. He will be a great doctor, perhaps, he comforted himself, or a scientist. With his eyes closed, he dozed under the warmth of the fur-lined robe.

But there came another day when he no longer saw the

young man's head at the window. And a few days later, he heard a knock at the door.

"Come in," he called. He stood up, holding the robe so that it would not slip off his thin shoulders.

The door opened and there stood his good neighbor.

"Oh, it's you," he said. He waited. Suddenly he knew what was coming.

Timidly, she said, "My son—"

He nodded, grimly.

She twisted her hands together. "He cannot sleep. He cannot study. He dreams all the night long. He longs for a fur coat." The good woman began to cry. "He says he will surely die if he cannot have a coat of fur. Oh please, sir, can you help him?"

Thoughtfully, he answered, "I think, perhaps, I can."

The old man wrapped his fur robe closely around him and followed the woman across the yard and up the stairs to the boy's room.

True enough, the boy looked near death. His eyes were dark holes in his face. But the old man pretended not to notice how the boy looked at the robe.

"I have come to save your life," he said, and smiled thinly at the boy's cry of delight. But he was in no hurry to take off his coat. He picked up a book that lay open on the desk. He looked at the papers lying there. Then he grunted and sat down.

"You are a smart boy," he said. "You have a good head. It should take you where you want to go—if you will let it."

The boy nodded, impatiently. His eyes were fastened to the fur-lined coat.

"Long ago, my father told me a story," said the old man. "And I am going to tell it to you."

. . . Once there was a snake. One day the snake was coiled up happily in his favorite spot when his tail thumped him from behind.

"Who's that?" asked the head sleepily.

"It's me," said the tail, "your tail."

The head opened his eyes and looked at the tail. "What's the matter?" he said. "Why do you thrash around like that?"

"I'm thrashing around because it seems to me that you've been leading us around long enough. It's my turn."

"You?" said the head. "But you cannot think. How can you lead us anywhere?"

"Maybe I can't think," said the tail, "but I can feel. And I feel very deeply. I feel it is my turn to be the leader for a change."

"All right," said the sleepy head. "If you feel you must, well you must, I suppose. Go ahead."

Well, the tail could feel all right, but he couldn't see, and he couldn't think. So he began dragging the snake into all sorts of places. Through a swamp and a nasty blackberry bramble. Up a tree of thorns and down again. The poor snake's head bumped along behind. His eyes were scratched and his fangs were at the wrong end when he needed them most. Finally the poor head had been bounced around so much that he scarcely had anything left to think with. And since the tail never did have anything to think with to begin with, he led the head into a bad spot and WHAM! That was the end of the snake—both head and tail . . .

The boy looked down at his feet.

"Like the snake," the old man said, "a man is born with a part for thinking and a part for feeling. When the head is doing its job, this works out pretty well. But when he lets his feelings do all his thinking for him, then maybe he's wearing a tail where his head should be."

And the old man got up, said, "Good day," and, clasping his fur coat closely about him, went home.

"We Will Hear"

The Israelites took the Ten Commandments into their hearts and the responsibilities that went with them onto their shoulders.

They said: *"Na—aseh v'nishma!"* We will do and we will hear.

Around these commandments, the Ten Words, they built their way of life. It became their religion. Today this religion is called Judaism, and the people who live by it are Jews.

It is your religion.

This Judaism of yours is an inheritance which has come to you from almost 4000 years ago. It belongs to you. But it is not something which you *have*. It is something which you *do*.

It is something which you can lose, but which you cannot give away. Something which you can keep but you cannot hide.

And you keep it by *doing*.

The Ten Commandments are the pillars upon which Judaism rests. The Law of the Jewish people, the Torah, started with the Ten Commandments, and almost all of it is concerned with *doing*. "Do not do unto others what is hateful to you."

These words seem so simple that almost everyone knows them by heart, and anyone can say them standing on one foot!

But the test is not merely to know, but to do.

Many have wondered how it is that a people who were not a nation outlived so many nations that were strong.

Perhaps it is because the Torah, though its meaning sounds simple, is exceedingly wise. The Torah, everyone knows, is the heart of Judaism. As long as this heart beats, the Jewish people live in strength, no matter what happens.

Or perhaps Judaism grew to be one of the strong religions of the world because in the Ten Commandments is the secret of peace on earth.

What the Ten Commandments really say is—respect God and respect life. Respect your parents, your sisters and brothers, your husband or your wife, your servants, your animals, your neighbors, and the stranger within your gates —and respect all that belongs to them.

And more, they say—respect yourself; through rest and work, through doing and understanding . . .

Religion has a special meaning for the Jewish people. And that special meaning is to help each person live his life in the best way he can—for himself, for his people, and for all mankind.

This is SOMETHING IMPORTANT.

Learn to say again in the words of your ancestors who stood at the foot of Mount Sinai:

"Na—aseh v'nishma!"

"We shall do and we shall understand." The world will be a better place because you live in it.

The
Ten
Commandments

I

I am the Lord your God who brought you out of
the land of Egypt, out of the house of bondage

II

You shall have no other gods—only Me.

You shall not make for yourself a sculptured image, any likeness of what is in the heavens above, or on the earth below, or in the waters below the earth. You shall not bow down to them or serve them. For I the Lord your God am an impassioned God, visiting the guilt of the fathers upon the children, upon the third and upon the fourth generations of those who reject Me, but showing kindness to the thousandth generation of those who love Me and keep My Commandments.

III

You shall not swear falsely by the name of the Lord your God; for the Lord will not clear one who swears falsely by His name.

IV

Remember the Sabbath day and keep it holy.

Six days you shall labor and do all your work,
but the seventh day is a Sabbath of the Lord
your God: you shall not do any work—you, your
son or daughter, your male or female slave, or
your cattle, or the stranger who is within your
settlements. For in six days the Lord made heav-
en and earth and sea, and all that is in them, and
He rested on the seventh day; therefore the Lord
blessed the Sabbath day and hallowed it.

V

Honor your father and mother, that you may long endure on the land which the Lord your God is giving you.

VI

You shall not murder.

VII

You shall not commit adultery.

VIII

You shall not steal.

IX

You shall not bear false witness against your neighbor.

X

You shall not covet your neighbor's house; you shall not covet your neighbor's wife, or his servant, or anything that is your neighbor's.

UNION GRADED SERIES
EDITED BY
ALEXANDER M. SCHINDLER, *Director of Education*
UNION OF AMERICAN HEBREW CONGREGATIONS